# Movie
## Themes
volume 2

VOLONTÈ&CO

Visit our website:
**www.volonte-co.com**
**info@volonte-co.com**

*Copertina di:* MORGANA

*Arrangements & Engravings by* ROBERTO BELLESI

# Anonimo Veneziano

Music by S. Cipriani

# Chariots Of Fire

Music by Vangelis

8

# Dos Gardenias

Lyrics and Music by I. Carillo

Dal 𝄋 al ⊕
poi CODA

# Ebb Tide

Lyrics by C.SIGMAN

Music by R. MAXWELL

# Eye Of The Tiger

Lyrics and Music by F. Sullivan / J. Peterik

# Footloose

Lyrics and Music by D. Pitchford / K. Loggins

**Rock Beat**

# Halleluya

Lyrics and Music by L. Cohen

**Moderatamente Lento**

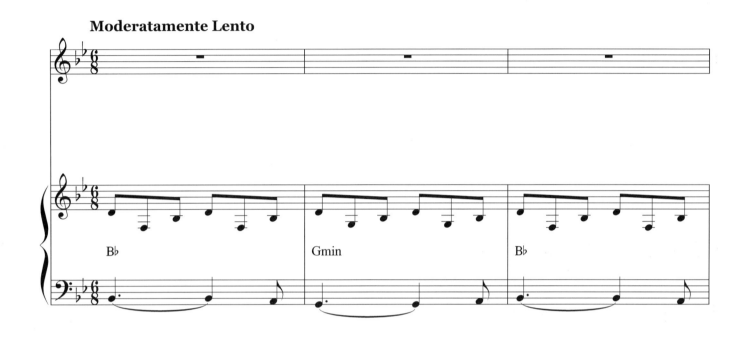

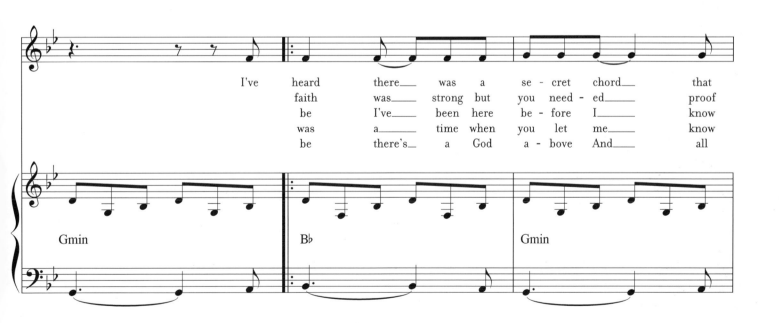

I've heard there___ was a se - cret chord___ that
faith was___ strong but you need - ed___ proof
be I've___ been here be - fore I___ know
was a___ time when you let me___ know
be there's___ a God a - bove And___ all

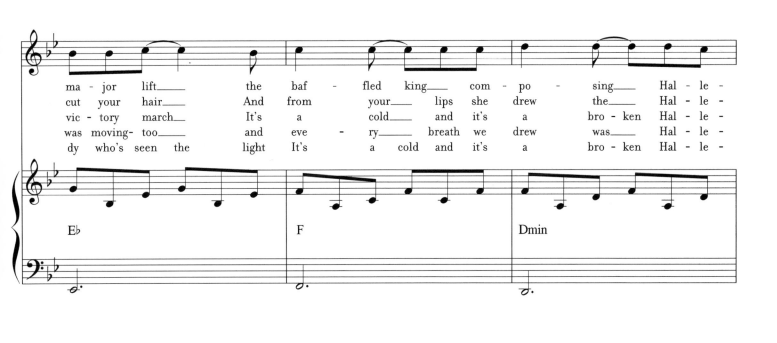

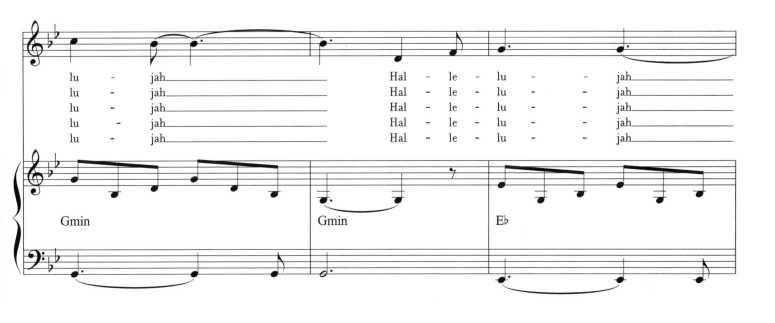

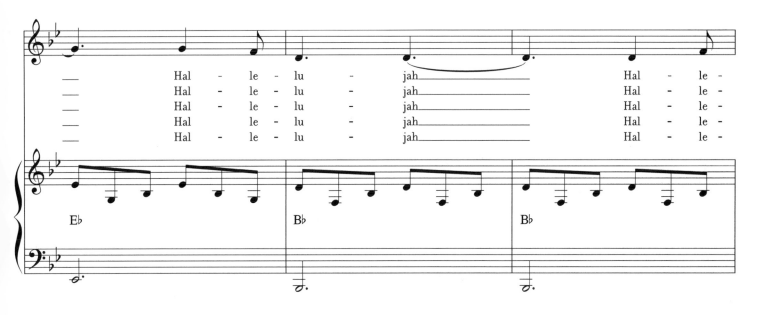

# I Will Always Love You

Lyrics and Music by D. Parton

# Il Postino

Music by L. Bacalov

**Moderato con molta espressione**

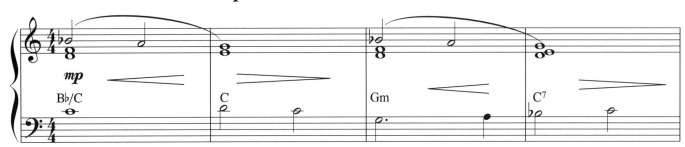

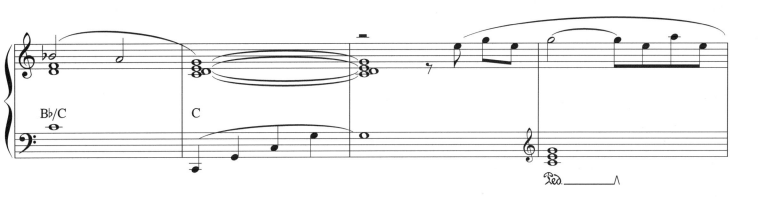

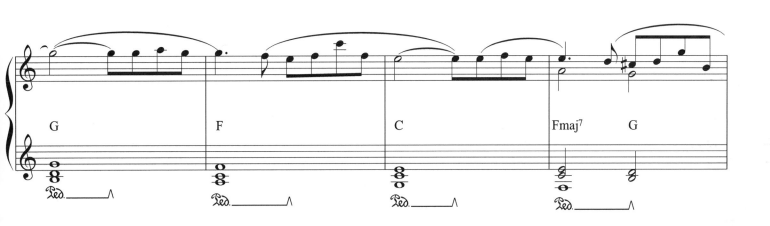

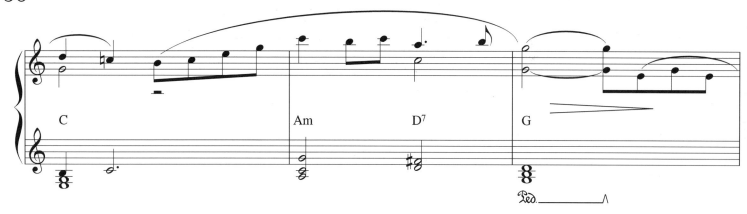

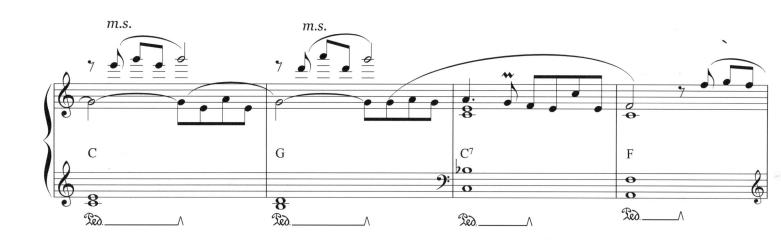

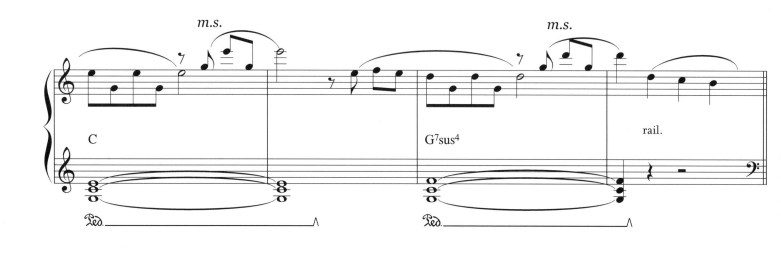

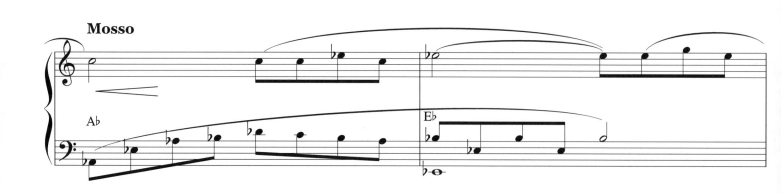

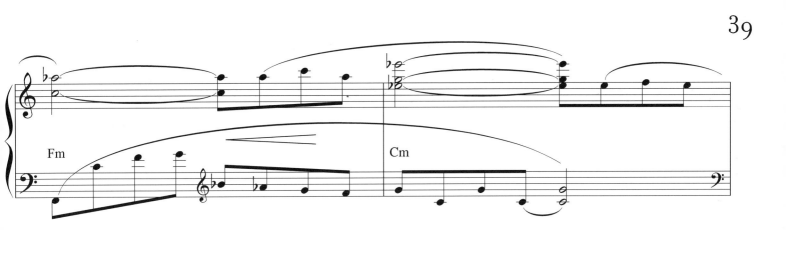

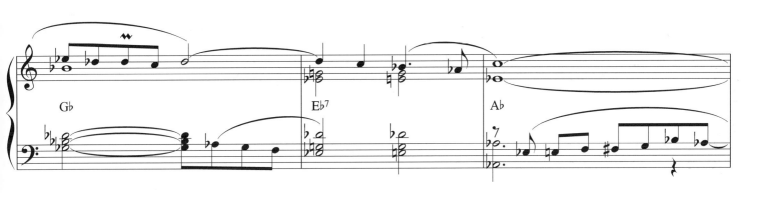

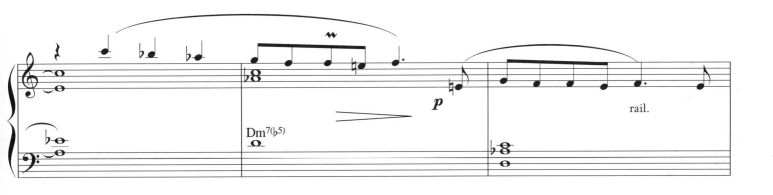

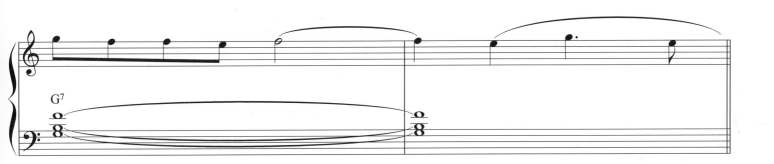

**A Tempo**

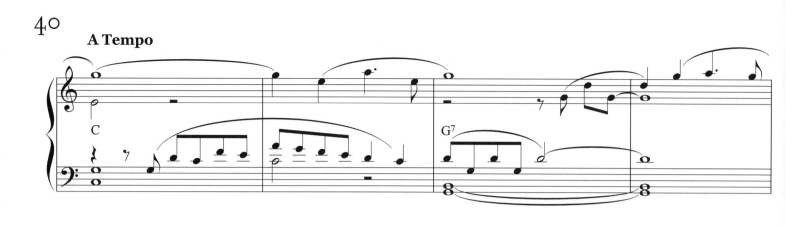

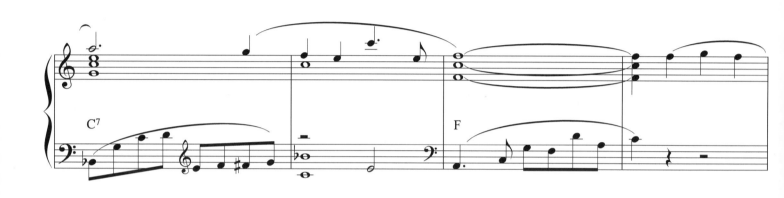

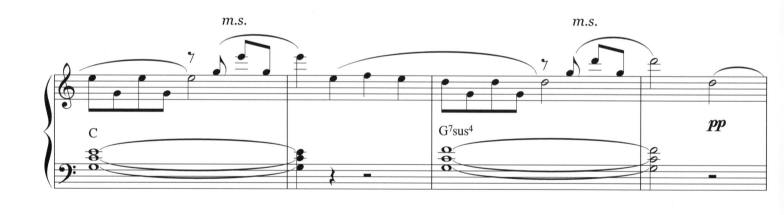

# La Dolce Vita

Lyrics and Music by E. Verde / N. Rota

# Love Is a Many Splendored Thing

Music by S. Fain

# Mamma Mia

Lyrics and Music by S. Anderson/B. Goran/B. Andersson/B. K. Ulvaeus

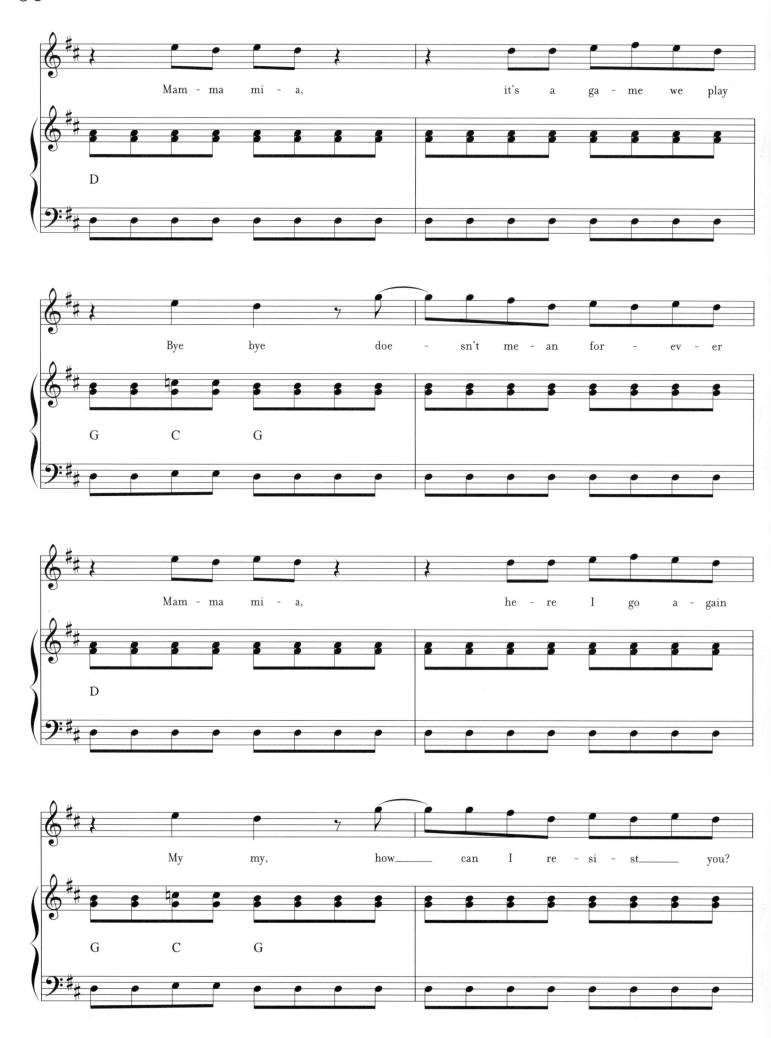

# Maple Leaf Rag

Music by S. Joplin

**Ragtime**

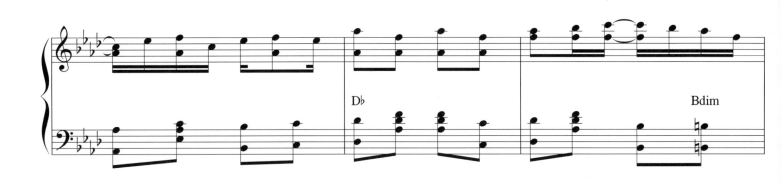

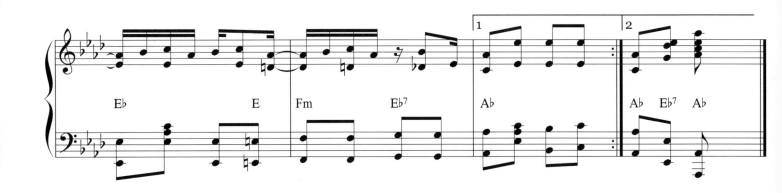

# Moon River

Lyrics and Music by H. Mancini / J. Mercer

# My Heart Will Go On

Lyrics by W. Jennings

Music by J. Horner

way. You are safe in my heart, and my heart will go

on and on.

Oh

# Now We Are Free

Lyrics and Music by H. Zimmer / L. Gerrard / K. Badelt

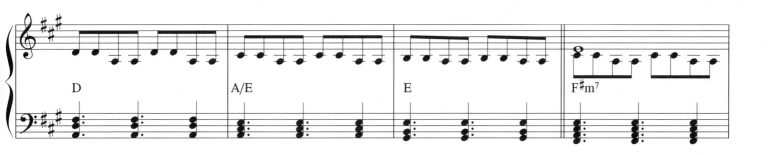

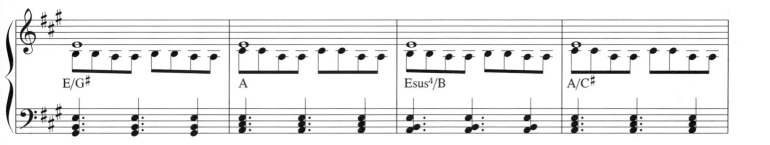

# Otto E Mezzo

Lyrics and Music by E. Fornai / N. Rota

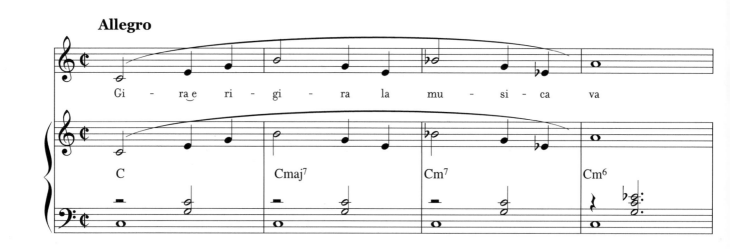

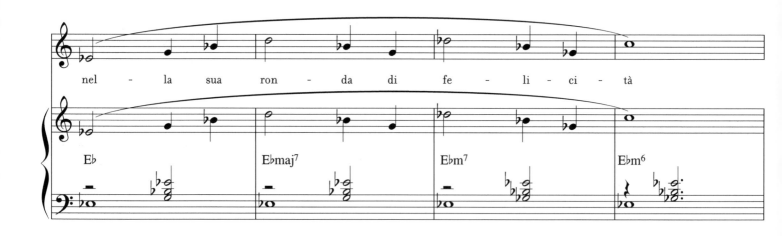

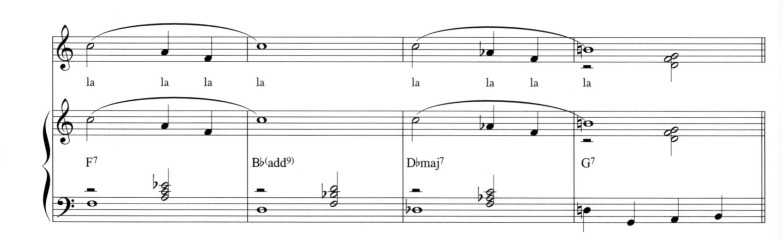

# Over The Rainbow

Lyrics by E. Y. Harburg

Music by H. Arlen

# Profondo Rosso

Music by Goblins

**Allegro Moderato**

# Singin' In The Rain

Lyrics by A. Freed

Music by N. H. Brown

# The Mission

Music by E. Morricone

# The Never Ending Story

Lyrics and Music by G. Moroder / K. Forsey

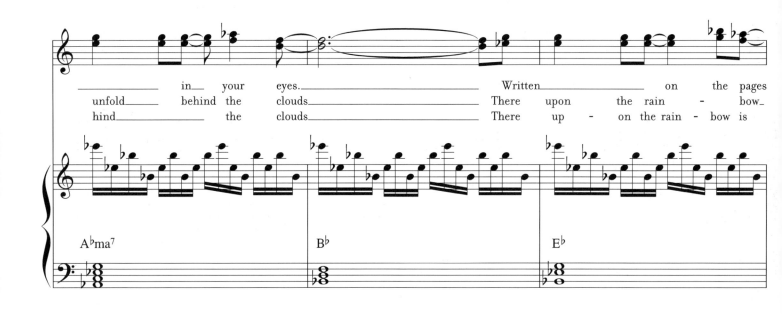

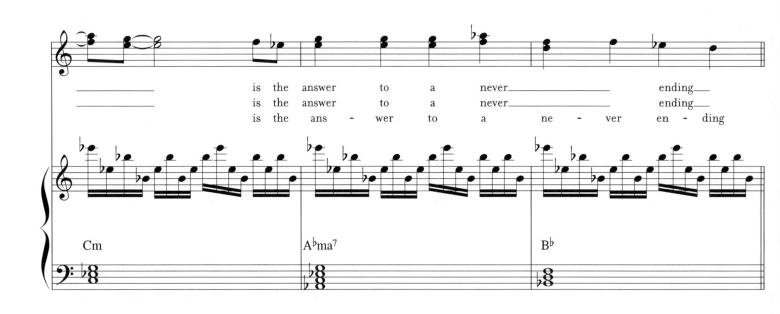

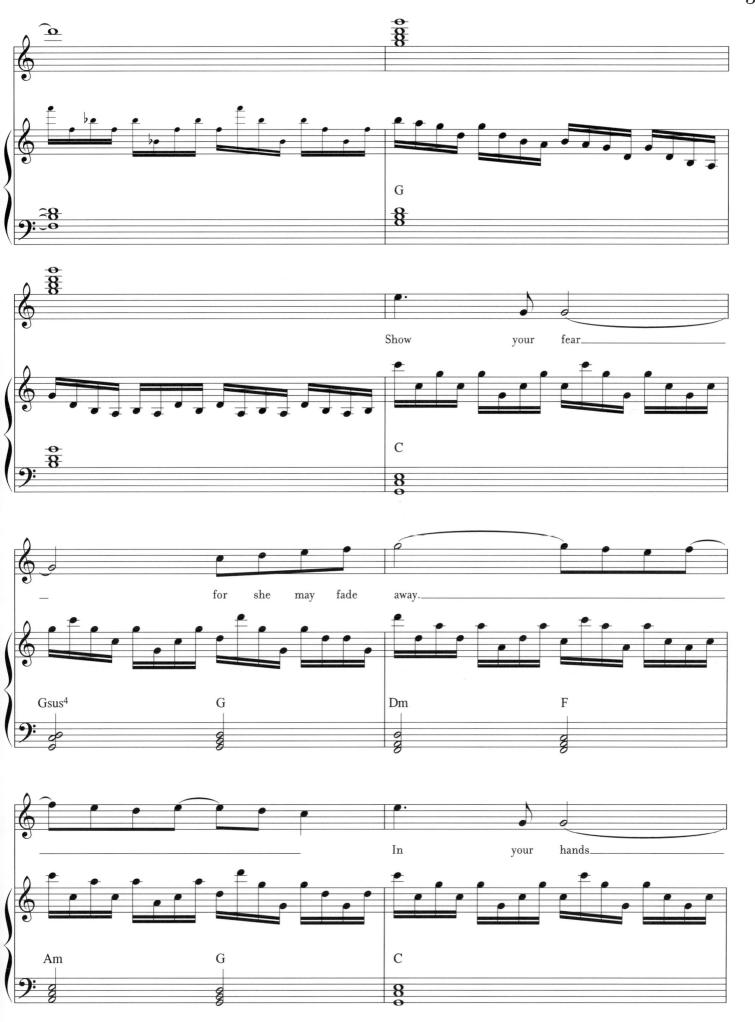

# The Untouchables

Music by E. Morricone

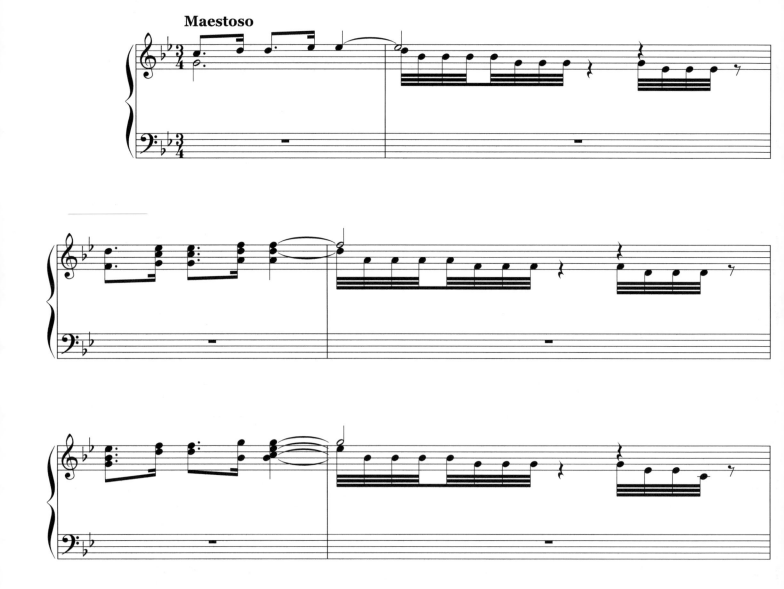

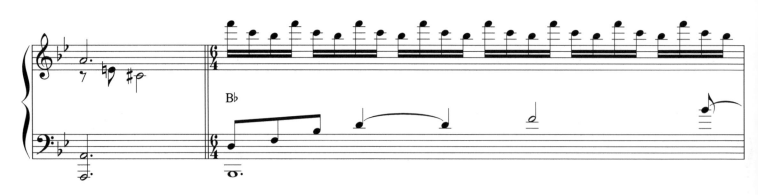

# Unchained Melody

Lyrics by H. Zaret

Music by A. North

# Up Where We Belong

Lyrics and Music by B. Sainte-Marie / J. Nitzsche / W. Jennings

Love lift us up where we be-long____ Where the

ea - gles cry,____ on a moun - tain high____

Love lift us up where we be-long____ Far from the

**Repeat and libitum**

world we know____ where the clear winds blow____